WHAT A GREAT TEAM!

by F. Isabel Campoy
illustrated by Kevin Rechin

Orlando Boston Dallas Chicago San Diego

Visit *The Learning Site!*
www.harcourtschool.com

Hi! Do you want
to play?

Daddy, may I play?

3

Hi! Do you want
to play?

Yes! Let's play!

Can we play, too?

Yes! Let's all play
together!

What a great team!